D0490818

EDINBURGH
& West Lothian
A LANDSCAPE FASHIONED BY GEOLOGY

©Scottish Natural Heritage 2003

ISBN 1 85397 327 0

A CIP record is held at the British Library
HS3K0303

Acknowledgements

Author: David McAdam

Text on pages 26 and 27: Allison Grant

Text on page 30: Alan McKirdy (SNH)

Series editor: Alan McKirdy (SNH)

Photography

T.S. Bain/BGS front cover, back cover, frontspiece, 5 left, 5 right, 6 left, 7 top, 7 bottom, 8, 13 top, 14, 16, 18 left, 18 right, 19 top, 19 bottom, 21, 23, 24, 26, 27, 28, 29, **M.A.E. Browne** 31 left, **L. Gill/SNH** 22, **F.I. Mactaggart/BGS** 10 top, **P&A. MacDonald/SNH** 11 left, 12, **The Trustees of the National Museums of Scotland** 30 bottom.

Illustrations

C. Ellery 2, 3, 6 right, 9, 11 right, 15 bottom, 17, 25 bottom, **I. McIntosh** contents page, **The Natural History Museum, London** 4, **Royal Society of Edinburgh (Transactions 12, plate 6)** 20, **Scottish Academic Press plc** top 30 top.

Further copies of this book and other publications can be obtained from:

The Publications Section,
Scottish Natural Heritage,
Battleby, Redgorton, Perth PH1 3EW
Tel 01738 444177 Fax:01738 827411
E-mail: pubs@snh.gov.uk
Web site: http://www.snh.org.uk

Front cover image:
Salisbury Crags and Arthur's Seat
from Blackford Hill, Edinburgh

Back cover image:
Samson's Ribs, Arthur's Seat, Edinburgh

EDINBURGH & West Lothian

A Landscape Fashioned by Geology

by

David McAdam

Edinburgh skyline from Rest-and-be-thankful, Corstorphine Hill

Contents

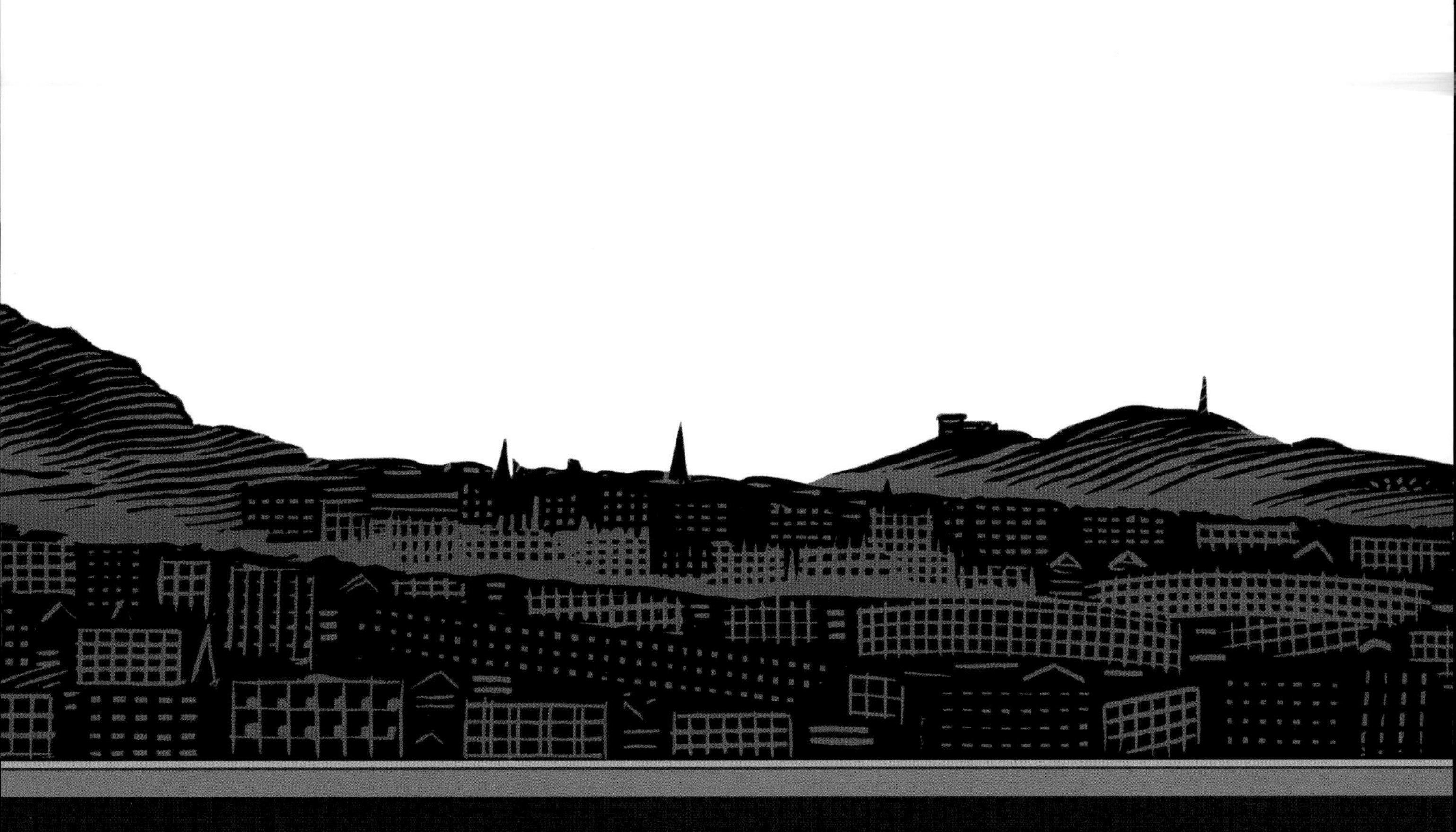

Edinburgh, called the `Athens of the North' because of its classical architecture, is said like Rome to be built on seven hills - Castle Hill, Calton Hill, Arthur's Seat, Corstorphine Hill, Craiglockhart Hill, Blackford Hill and the Braid Hills. What links all these hills is their igneous or volcanic origin; they are all made of hard durable rock which has resisted subsequent erosion to leave them standing as prominent features of the landscape. But there are also ridges and hollows, gorges and flat plains. Edinburgh's landscape took over 400 million years to reach its present shape. This booklet explains how.

Edinbu

RECENT TIMES	**Present day.** New 'New Town' at Edinburgh Park. City By-pass open; coal and oil-shale industries closed. **80 years ago.** Midlothian Coalfield and West Lothian oil-shale field at peak, coal and massive red spent shale bings. **220 years ago.** Edinburgh New Town round drumlin ridge of George Street; built from sandstone quarried at Craigleith and Hailes and transported by canal from West Lothian; Nor' Loch drained; limestone quarrying, as at Gilmerton and Cousland. **800 years ago.** Edinburgh Old Town developed round Castle Rock and down glacial tail feature of Royal Mile; lowland forests on glaciated landscape cleared and lochs drained for agriculture. Coal mining starts. **1,900 years ago.** Glaciated landscape, shallow lochs marshy and silting up; Roman occupation of ports at Cramond and Inveresk.
QUATERNARY THE 'ICE AGE' **2.4 million years ago up to and including recent times**	**5,000 to 4,000 years.** Sea at level comparable with present day; Neolithic hunters colonised the area building strongholds on volcanic hills; away from lowland forests and swamps with their predators. **6,500 years.** Sea level at 8m above present day forming an extensive platform with prominent cliff all along the coast. **9,000 to 8,000 years.** Peat accumulates as climate becomes warm and wet. **11,000 to 10,000 years.** Climate cools again to arctic conditions; sea level falls to present-day level or below. **13,000 years.** Ice had retreated to the Highlands and had vanished from the Southern Uplands; melt water cut new valleys and gorges, transported glacial debris and deposited it as sands and gravels, as in the Esk Valley, or as silts and clays in lochs and along sea-shores; sea level is up to 45m higher than present day. **19,000 years.** Ice, 5 kilometres thick, extends many miles east of the present coastline. **27,000 years.** Last advance of the 'Ice Age' as ice builds up in the Highlands and Southern Uplands. **2.4 million years.** Climate cools and 'Ice Age' begins.
TERTIARY **65 to 2.4 million years ago**	**62 million years.** Weathering and erosion largely fashion present-day river systems; Volcanic activity in west of Scotland; no record of any geological events in Edinburgh & West Lothian.
CRETACEOUS **135 to 65 million years ago**	**80 million years.** Warm shallow temperate seas fringe the land, with chalk deposited across Scotland, but later removed by erosion.
JURASSIC **205 to 135 million years ago**	Climate on land is warm and humid.
PERMIAN - TRIASSIC **295 to 205 million years ago**	Climate on land is arid; desert conditions widespread.
CARBONIFEROUS **355 to 295 million years** **Scotland sits astride the equator**	**Throughout Carboniferous.** Intrusion of dykes and sills as at Salisbury Crags and Corstorphine Hill. **305 million years.** Movements within the Earth's crust, cause folding, faulting, uplift of the crust and subsequent erosion. **315 million years.** Forests established to give another series of coal seams. **320 million years.** Large rivers lay down thick sandstones. **330 million years.** Thick forests repeatedly blanket the land, their peaty remains turning to numerous coal seams. **335 million years.** Corals flourish in tropical seas and rich marine life in carbonate muds, producing thick beds of limestone full of fossils. **340 million years.** Rich algal life flourish in coastal lagoons, producing oil-shales; while river deltas lay down thick sandstones as at Craigleith and Hailes. **345 million years.** Small volcanoes begin erupting lavas and ash on land and under the sea, as at Arthur's Seat, Castle Rock, Craiglockhart Hill. Volcanic activity and earthquakes continue throughout the next 50 million years. **355 million years.** Semi-arid coastal plain at times flooded by the sea. Limy beds with shrimps, mussels and other fossils.
DEVONIAN **410 to 355 million years**	**370 million years.** Widespread alluvial plain established, inland desert with extensive areas of sand dunes, leaving sandstones along north of the Pentland Hills. **410 million years.** Large volcanoes producing lava and debris flows built the Pentland Hills, Braid Hills and Blackford Hill. Semi-arid climate with large river systems depositing thick beds of sand and gravel. Primitive plants and fish fossilised in lake deposits.
SILURIAN **440 to 410 million years**	**420 million years.** The earth moves when Scotland collides with England as the Iapetus Ocean in-between closes. Extensive folding, faulting, and uplift of the crust from the Southern Uplands and subsequent erosion ensues. The Southern Upland Fault is created as a boundary between the Southern Uplands and the Midland Valley.
ORDOVICIAN **510 to 440 million years**	Great thickness of muds and sands accumulate in the Iapetus Ocean, which separated Laurentia (including the land now called Scotland) from Avalonia (including the land now called England). No record of any earlier geological events in Edinburgh & West Lothian.

Geological Map of Edinburgh & West Lothian

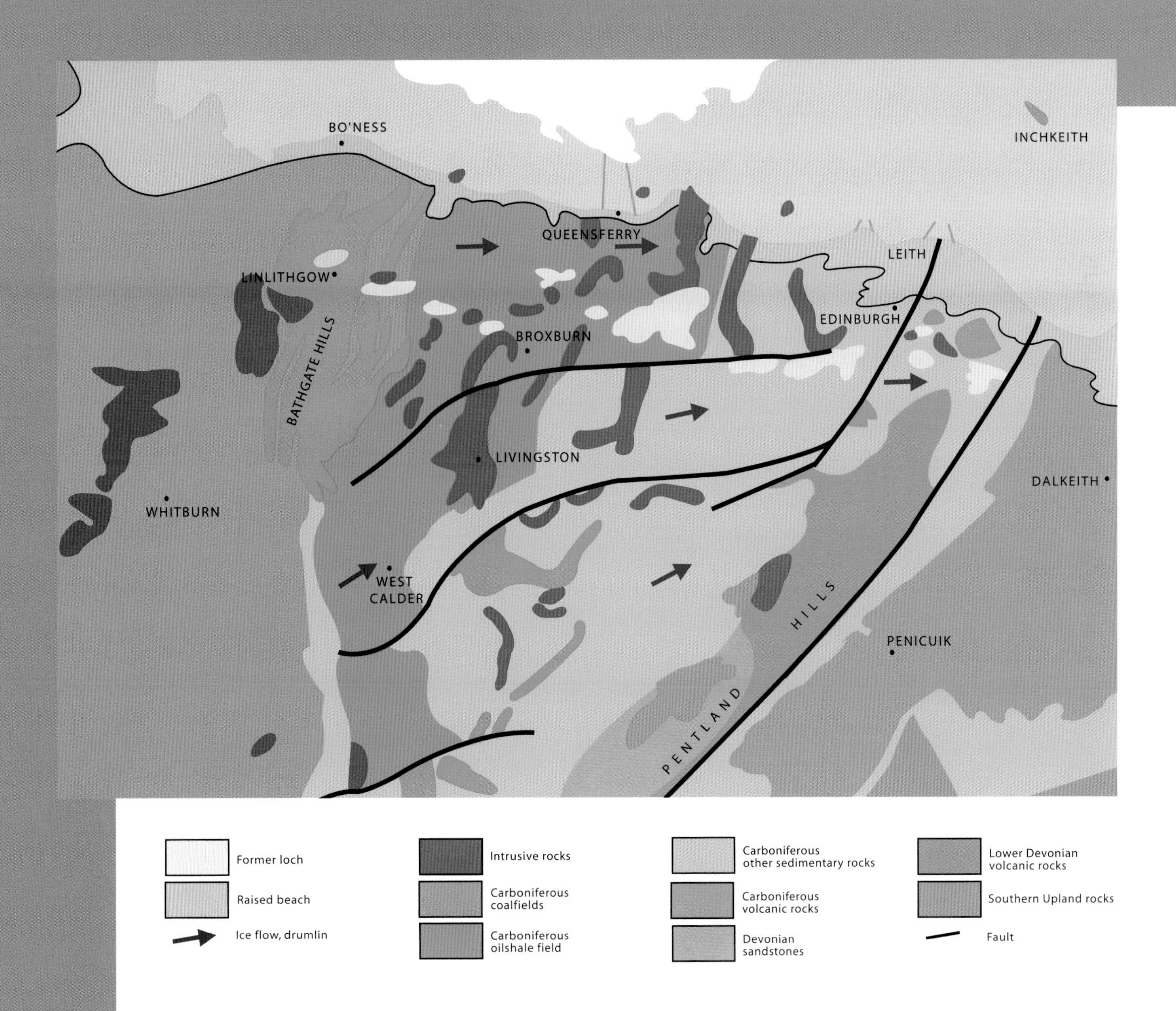

Volcanoes Create the Seven Hills

Volcanoes in the heart of the city of Edinburgh? Yes, but Edinburgh's volcanoes are very ancient. Some erupted around 400 million years ago. The most important volcanoes, however, were active about 350 million years ago. The good news is that they will not erupt again.

The best preserved of these ancient volcanoes is Arthur's Seat. As we shall see, erosion has dug deep into the heart of the volcano laying open its inside structure so that the vents, the lava flows and the ash falls are clearly visible.

Some 350 million years ago, the area we now call Edinburgh basked on a flat tropical shore, with tree-fringed, fish-filled lagoons, very much like the American Gulf Coast of today; and not a hill in sight!

The calm was rudely shattered by the eruption of a volcano where the Castle now stands. Ash was tossed out and lava spread across the plain. The eruption was short-lived, but the peace was short-lived too.

Fresh eruptions arose further east where Holyrood Park now lies. Violent explosions threw volcanic ash high into the turbulent atmosphere; at least a dozen eruptions poured out flows of lava which cooled to a black rock called basalt.

The volcanic cone built up several hundred metres above the surrounding plain. Quieter spells between eruptions allowed life to recolonise the area, only disturbed by ash falls settling into the shallow water. The position of vents moved from eruption to eruption as the molten rock (magma) found new ways to reach the surface. Each vent became filled with a mixture of blocks of lava and volcanic ash known as vent agglomerate.

Vent agglomerate, Queen's Drive

After a while the volcano became totally extinct, the land subsided, the volcano sank under the sea and it was buried under thousands of metres of sediments.

The spectacular rock feature known as Samson's Ribs (back cover) was formed inside the volcano. Molten rock left in the volcanic vent at the end of the eruption cooled slowly and formed 6-sided columns of basalt. These are very similar to the columns seen in Fingal's Cave on Staffa and in the Giant's Causeway in Ireland. Because they now lie on the steep side of Arthur's Seat, they are liable to fall, as frost action forces the columns apart.

Intrusions – Volcanoes That Did Not Quite Make It

Salisbury Crags

Molten rock, or magma, does not always succeed in reaching the earth's surface. Forcing a way through layered strata is not easy. Sometimes magma finds joints or fault cracks to travel towards the surface; at other times it seeks an easier route along the bedding between layers of strata. Such diversions can allow basalt magma to cool before reaching the surface. The magma cools and solidifies into rock called dolerite. This layered sandwich of hard intruded magma between beds of softer sedimentary strata is called a sill.

By far the most spectacular one in the area is Salisbury Crags, where the intrusive form of the hard sill forms the crags and the strata above and below can be clearly seen. Quarrying the crags to pave the streets of London in the nineteenth century left their faces sharper than nature fashioned them. Conservation interests fortunately halted this practice.

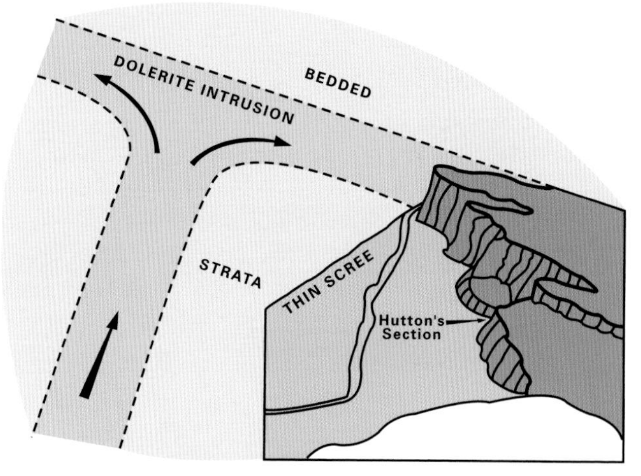

Laccolith, Black Hill

Other dolerite sills form most of the hills on the west side of Edinburgh such as Corstorphine Hill, Turnhouse Hill, Mons Hill, Dalmahoy Hill and Binny Craig, all pocked with ancient or modern quarries for building and road stone. Quarrymen call this rock 'whin'. It is no coincidence that in spring these hills are ablaze with yellow gorse or 'whin' which thrives on the thin stony dolerite soil.

Dykes are narrow vertical intrusions that fill cracks in the strata. Like all intrusions, the rock cracks on cooling to give a joint pattern as at Beecraigs.

Black Hill is distinguished from the other Pentland Hills by its regular oval shape. This is because it is not formed of volcanic lava and ash, but is a dome-shaped intrusion known as a laccolith, made of a pale rock called felsite.

Dyke, Beecraigs, with cooling joints

The Arthur's Seat Volcano Today

Whinny Hill and Arthur's Seat from Calton Hill

The secrets of the Arthur's Seat volcano and the Salisbury Crags sill could have remained hidden in the bowels of the earth forever. However, after the volcano became extinct and was buried, massive forces produced by the drifting and collision of the continents pushed up and folded the sedimentary and volcanic strata to form mountains and folded them into basins and domes. Arthur's Seat was tilted to the east, and erosion, by good chance, has left the volcano cut across with its various components exposed to view, as can be superbly seen from the Calton Hill. Calton Hill is, itself, a displaced fragment of the Arthur's Seat volcano.

The twin summits of the Lion's Head and the Lion's Haunch are all that is left of the central vents of the volcano. Only half of the volcanic cone is preserved to the east as Whinny Hill. Alternating hard lava flows and soft volcanic ash bands give the hill its tilted stepped form. Rock faces at St Anthony's Chapel and on the Queen's Drive show clearly the alternating layers of ash and lava with this eastward tilt.

Around the same time as the Arthur's Seat volcano was active other volcanoes formed the Craiglockhart Hills, the Bathgate Hills and Corston Hill.

Eruptions during a volcanic episode, some 50 million years earlier gave rise to the rocks now forming the Pentland Hills, the Braid Hills and Blackford Hill.

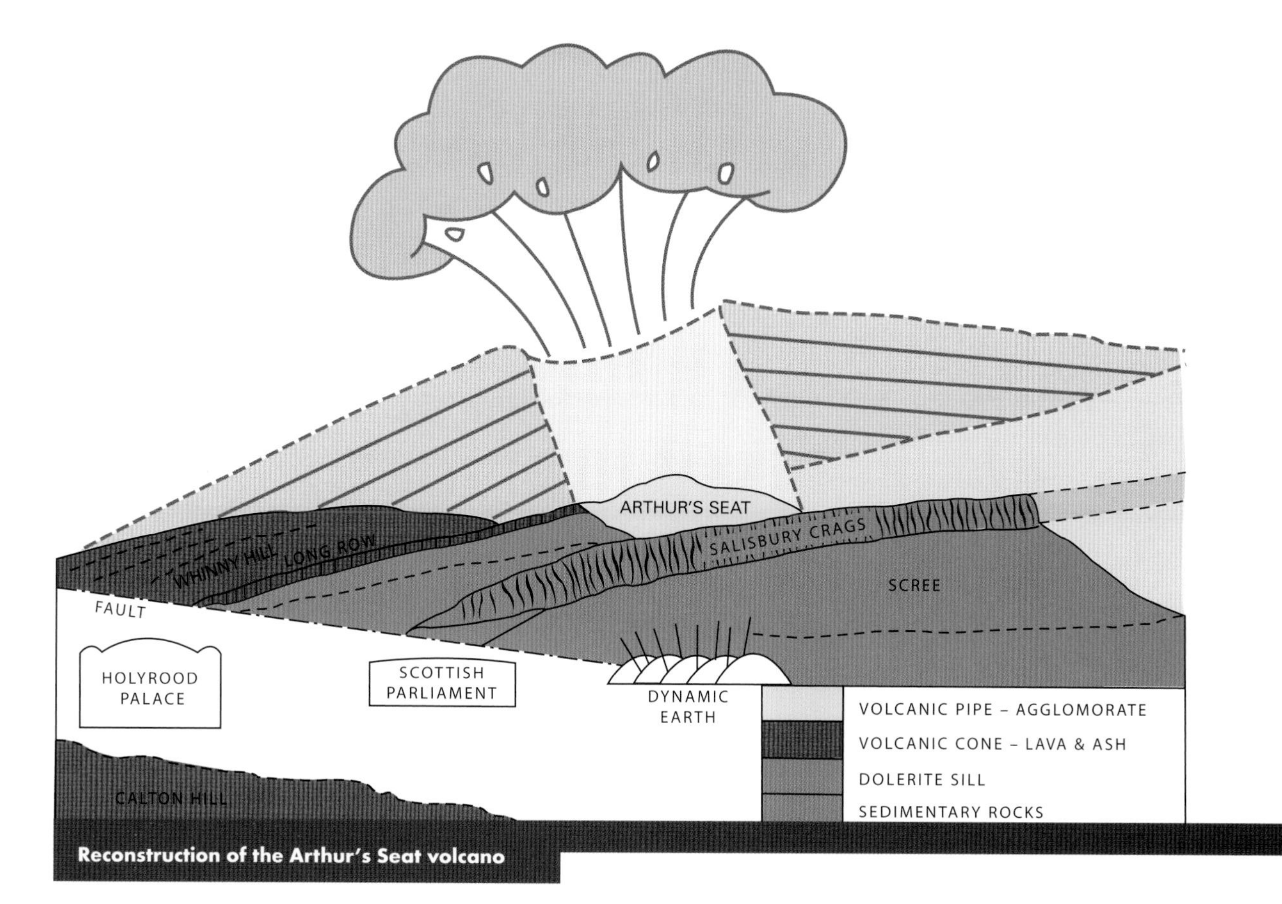

Reconstruction of the Arthur's Seat volcano

Sedimentary rocks are mostly softer than igneous rocks, so they tend not to form prominent features of the landscape. However, in their own way the sedimentary rocks are equally as important as the volcanic rocks in understanding the landscape and the geology that dictated its present form.

Strata are layers of sedimentary rocks. Each different bed is formed in a particular environment that gives it its special appearance.

The oldest sediments in the area are thick red sandstones called the Upper Old Red Sandstone (Upper Devonian) which formed 370 million years ago when the area was barren mountains and deserts. Sand, eroded from even older rocks, was blown by hot winds into valleys scoured by flash floods often forming short-lived lochs.

Old red sandstones, Dreghorn Spur

Devonian desert landscape

Landscapes are constantly changing. The Old Red Sandstone mountains were worn down to plains with shallow lagoons and seas throughout the great period called the Carboniferous (coal-bearing) when most of the rocks underlying Edinburgh and West Lothian were formed.

The Carboniferous period was characterised by rapidly changing environments, leading to rapidly alternating layers of rock or strata. These are often in regular cycles repeating the same sequence of rocks known as a cyclothem.

Nature is never perfect, so every cycle is different. Some beds in a cycle may be thin or missing because particular conditions never occurred at that time. Other beds may be thick because a certain environment persisted longer than usual.

Like rings on a tree, the variation of cycles can be matched from one area to another, particularly using the rich life preserved as fossils in some beds.

In different parts of the Carboniferous period different parts of the cycles were thick. Thus during two long eras the coal forests tended to last longer, giving sequences with thick coal seams. Tropical seas like those found today in the Caribbean, encouraged thick limestones with corals, shells and other fossil remains of the rich marine life.

Lagoons with organic-rich muds were repeatedly developed, giving rise to the oil-shales of West Lothian. Some sandstones were laid down along coastal beaches and dunes; others were formed by rivers and contain trees carried down during the floods. Thick, hard, fine-grained sandstones such as Craigleith and Hailes proved ideal as building stones.

Carboniferous strata, Joppa shore

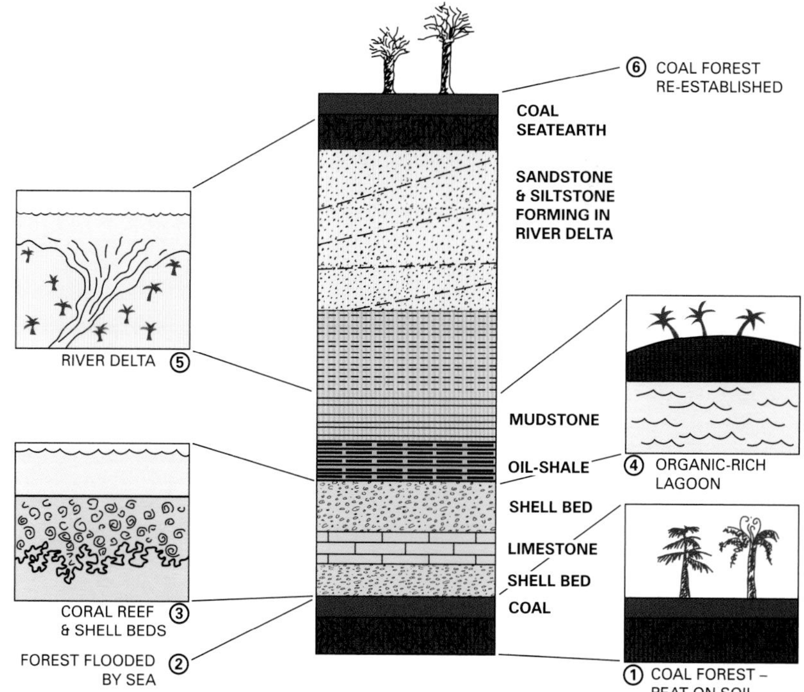

Formation of a Carboniferous cyclothem

Crag and tail of Edinburgh Castle and the Royal Mile

Like all of northern Britain during the last 2 million years Edinburgh and West Lothian have been repeatedly buried under an ice-cap hundreds of metres thick.

The latest ice-cap melted as recently as 15,000 years ago. As each ice-age began, ice built up in the Highlands and Southern Uplands, merged in the Midland Valley and flowed eastwards across the area. The weight of ice selectively eroded the softer sedimentary rocks, leaving the harder volcanic rocks as hills. All these hills have a tail to the east (lee) side, forming a feature known as a 'crag and tail'; the best example is Edinburgh Castle and the Royal Mile.

Long oval ridges, called drumlins, fashioned by ice, cover West Lothian and much of west and south Edinburgh. The ice also moulded the harder rocks as on Corstorphine Hill (page 31) and left scratches (striae) on the rocks as a record of its passage.

Material eroded by the ice was left as glacial till (boulder clay), a mixture of tough clay, rock-flour, made from ground-down mudstone and siltstone, together with rounded pebbles and boulders, the remains of the harder volcanic rocks, limestones or sandstones. Boulder clay covers much of the low ground in Edinburgh and West Lothian.

Melting of the ice produced vast amounts of water. This meltwater rapidly cut new channels to lower ground. Many were abandoned as further melting allowed lower channels to be cut, leaving dry valleys devoid of river or stream. Hence these channels are a common feature of our landscape.

Dry valley cut by meltwater, Carlops

Ice Age reconstruction

The meltwater carried heavy loads of sediment freed from the ice as it melted. The coarser parts – the boulder, pebbles and sands – were dropped as soon as the initial flood subsided to give widespread mounds and terraces of bedded sand and gravel, as in the valley of the Esk. The finer parts – the silts and clays – were carried on to be deposited in lochs and in the sea.

Lochs, Seas and Rivers – The Great Levellers

Raised beaches, Cramond

Hollows abounded in this ice-scoured landscape; water soon flowed in to form numerous lochs. Silt and clay, trapped by reed-beds filled these to form wide boggy marshes. All, except Duddingston Loch, have been drained to create flat areas. The largest lochs were at Corstorphine, Gogar and Turnhouse. The Borough Loch is now the Meadows; the Nor' Loch became Princes Street Gardens.

Sea-levels have risen and fallen several times since the end of the ice-age. This was due to two factors; ice taking water from the oceans, and the weight of ice pressing down the land which later rebounded. At the end of the ice age the sea along the Forth estuary stood around 40m higher than present; waves lapped against Calton Hill at London Road and on the doorsteps of the Scottish Parliament at Holyrood. Land below this was an estuarine mudflat blanketed with marine sands, silts and clays.

Fall of the sea to its present level occurred in fits and starts, sudden drops being followed by long standstills. The most significant standstill occurred about 6500 years ago producing a flat beach at about 8m above sea-level with an old sea-cliff behind; this can be seen today all along the coast from Bo'ness to Musselburgh.

Sudden drops in sea-levels caused the rivers to cut the gorges found along much of the River Almond, the Water of Leith and both the North Esk and South Esk. Debris eroded by rivers is laid down as alluvium, a flat plain of gravel, sand, silt and clay, bordering all the rivers and streams.

Thus was made the landscape bequeathed by nature. What man has done to it is the subject of the next part of the booklet. The distribution of the landscape-forming rocks and glacial deposits is as shown by the geological map on page 3, and the timetable of events that resulted in the present landscape of Edinburgh on page 2.

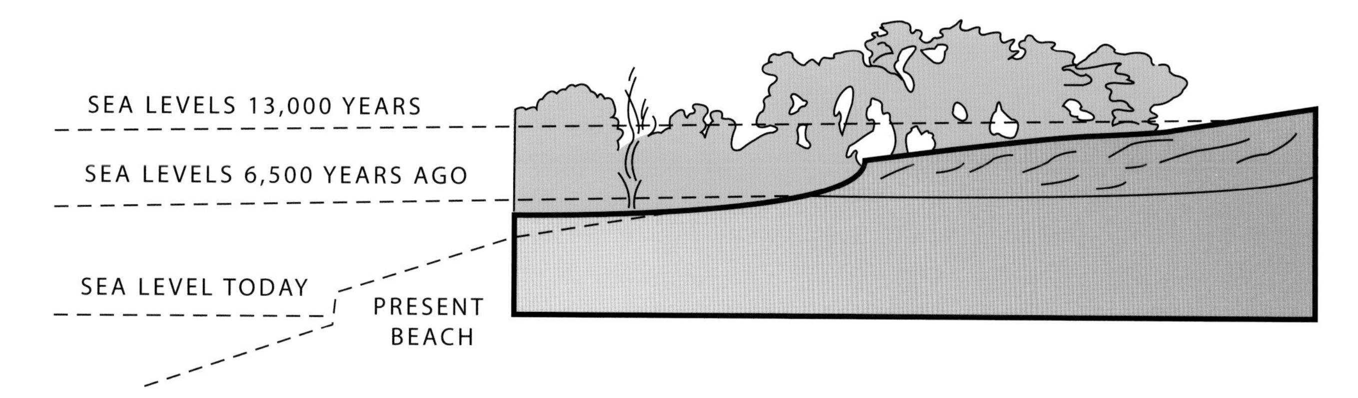

Reconstruction of sea-levels, Cramond

This tourist view, familiar to every visitor to Edinburgh, embodies many of the aspects that make up Edinburgh's landscape:

- Castle Rock is now recognised to be the eroded remains of a volcanic pipe which erupted 350 million years ago and cooled as a circular vertical plug of very hard dolerite rock.
- The even older bedded sedimentary rocks cut through by the volcano.
- The 'crag and tail' feature carved out by ice flowing from the west; the ice was forced over and round the hard volcanic plug forming the 'crag' and preserving softer sedimentary rocks in the 'tail' of the Royal Mile.
- Alluvial deposits in the bed of the Nor' Loch which filled the deep hollow carved out by ice diverted round the side of the Castle Rock; now laid out as Princes Street Gardens.
- Jumbled ground, the result of a landslip on the very steep slope left by the ice on the side of the tail.
- The castle buildings and wall making use of the strategic site created by the glaciated volcanic crag.
- The Old Town sited on the 'tail' where it could be easily surrounded by the city wall.
- The artificial embankment created to shield the sight and sound of the trains from the passers-by on Princes Street.

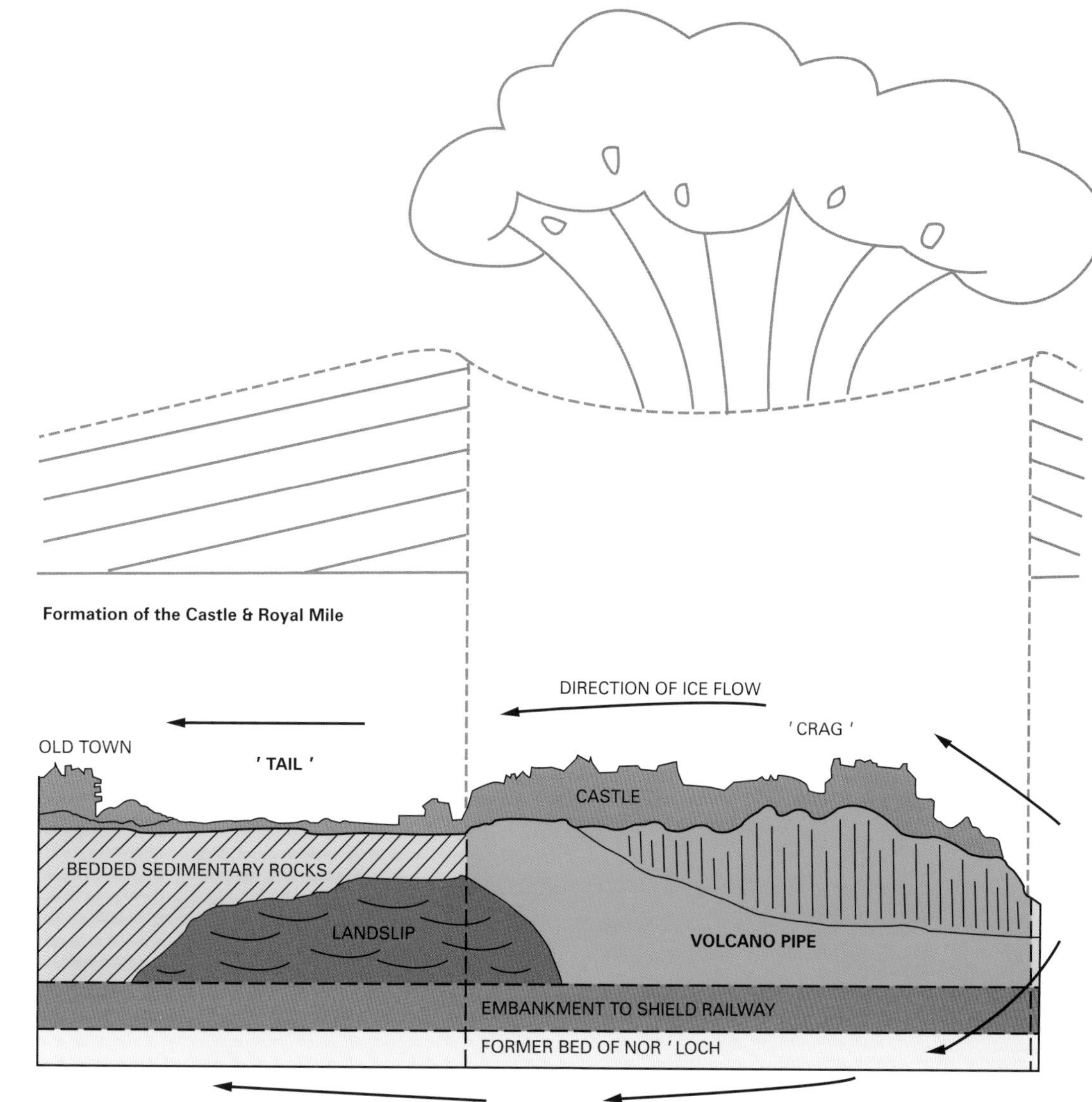

Formation of the Castle & Royal Mile

Mining & Quarrying – Man Alters Nature's Landscape

Far left: oil-shale miners' cottages at Winchburgh.
Left: Mining Sculpture at Newtongrange by Jake Harvey R.S.A.

From earliest times man has made use of the mineral bounty which nature provided, from prehistoric stone axeheads and knives, to whin chips to pave the motorways.

Some 800 years ago man realised that coal from seams within the rock strata would burn and could be used for heating and cooking. First excavations were from outcrops into valley sides. Then bell pits were dug down to mine small areas round the shaft.

Only in the past two centuries have shafts been sunk to mine coal seams at depths of hundreds or even up to a thousand metres. Coal mining produced the black conical spoil heaps (bings) once so prominent in the Esk valleys and around Bo'ness.

More recently opencast quarrying of coal seams has a dramatic, if temporary, impact on the landscape. Coal mining has now ceased in the Lothians; only a legacy of memories and landscaped spoil is left.

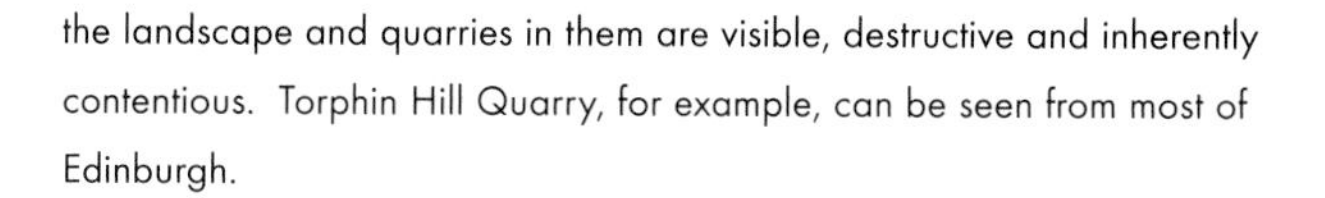

Above: Oil-shale bing, Broxburn

Right: Close-up of oil-shale

Limestone was quarried, and even mined for lime to improve arable land and for use in mortar and cement. This left a landscape littered with half-filled quarries, spoil heaps and lime kilns.

In the 1850s James 'Paraffin' Young founded a new industry when he developed the means to extract crude oil from oil-shale seams discovered in the strata of West Lothian. Processing the oil-shale to drive off the hydrocarbons left the same volume of oil-shale spoil as was mined. The resulting flat-topped red shale bings dominate the skyline of West Lothian though the associated collieries, distillation and refining plant are long since gone.

Road metal and aggregate for concrete demands large quarries in igneous rocks. As those rocks are hard, they form prominent features of the landscape and quarries in them are visible, destructive and inherently contentious. Torphin Hill Quarry, for example, can be seen from most of Edinburgh.

Glacial sands and gravels provide the essential raw materials for much of modern building and construction. Large pits in the Esk valley satisfy this demand but at the cost of swapping an interesting natural landscape for a flat restored pit floor.

Craigleith Quarry

When man first ventured into the area now called Lothian, it was blanketed with forests, much of the low ground was swampy and treacherous, while wolves and other wild animals roamed widely. The rocky volcanic hills which poked through the forest provided the only safe places for the first habitations. All that remain are traces of hill forts and early cultivation terraces as on the slopes of Arthur's Seat.

Over the centuries the forest was cleared for agriculture but the volcanic hills still provided the best-defended sites. The Old Town of Edinburgh formed round the Castle Rock, enclosed within a city wall making use of the steep-sided glacial crag-and-tail feature.

Expansion of the city became unavoidable, and the 'New Town' started in the late 18th century on the glaciated landscape to the North. The distinctive layout, for example of Princes Street, George Street and Queen Street area with their gardens was very much dictated by the form of a drumlin ridge.

Heriot Row

The sandstone quarries at Craigleith and Hailes were two of the many that provided sandstone blocks for the fine architecture of the New Town of Edinburgh. Both quarries are now filled in.

Further expansion into the suburbs at the end of the 19th and early 20th centuries swallowed up the rolling glaciated landscape. The new building was very much in harmony with the landscape giving the distinctive curving, up and down roads in places like Barnton, Morningside and Corstorphine.

Later building became less and less sympathetic to the natural landscape, culminating in multi-storey flats, constructed in a regular pattern regardless of the form of the land.

Walkers on Pentland Hills above Edinburgh

The volcanic hills not only form the prominent scenic parts of the landscape, their ruggedness has saved them from development, with the notable exception of the Castle Rock. Hence their almost universal use as parks for walking and other recreational activities. Arthur's Seat is the Queen's Park; Calton Hill, Craiglockhart Hill, Corstorphine Hill and Blackford Hill are all parks belonging to the city.

The Pentland Hills form a backdrop to Edinburgh's scenery, and also, in the Regional Park, its largest area for recreation. The volcanic hills and glaciated valleys have discouraged all but limited development in an area of upland scenery. (See pages 24 and 25).

The incised gorges provide undeveloped strips along river banks rivers with some interesting, scenic, even spectacular walks, more and more utilised for recreation as at Almondell and Calderwood Country Park on the River Almond. The Water of Leith walkway set an example for others such as in the River Avon.

Musselburgh Racecourse and Musselburgh Golf Course

Golf courses form one of the major land uses in the city. Their location is dictated very much by geology. Musselburgh is claimed as site of the oldest golf course in the world. There it was that the Royal & Ancient game evolved on the natural landscape of raised beach and sand dune. Similar conditions encouraged many courses to develop along the East Lothian coast. Later course designers were attracted to volcanic hills, such as the Braids courses, Craigmillar Park on Blackford Hill, Turnhouse on a dolerite sill, Merchants of Edinburgh on the Craiglockhart Hills, Lothianburn and Swanston on the slopes of the Pentlands. Other courses, such as Murrayfield and Barnton, utilised the undulating glaciated contours or the less exciting flat beds of former lochs such as Prestonfield and Carrick Knowe.

Unlike golf, many games demand a flat, level field. Nature provides this in the form of drained loch beds, the alluvial plains along rivers and streams, or raised beach terraces. Murrayfield Rugby Ground and Heart of Midlothian Football Ground are both sited on the bed of Corstorphine Loch. Hibernian Football Ground and Meadowbank Stadium are two of the many venues taking advantage of raised beach flats in the north of the city as does Edinburgh Racecourse. A loch flat at Turnhouse is used for Edinburgh airport.

Pentland Hills from Castlelaw Hill

This fine panoramic view displays the dramatic landscape of the Pentland Hills. The tops all owe their prominence to the hardness of the 400 million year old volcanic rocks, both lavas and ashes, of Devonian age.

The rocks are classified according to the minerals they contain. Trachytes and rhyolites tend to be pale orange or pink in colour, basalts and andesites dark grey or purple. The volcanic ashes form a soft rock called tuff.

Some of the more southerly Pentland Hills are made of Devonian red sandstones as old as the lavas. The heart of the Pentlands and the distant Southern Uplands are formed of folded sedimentary rocks of Silurian and Ordovician age, much older than any found in the Edinburgh area.

Glacial deposits obscure the softer sedimentary rocks which form the low ground. This valley from Balerno to Glencorse Reservoir, popular with walkers, was cut by glacial meltwater, overflowing from West Lothian into the valley of the Esk. An alluvial flat borders the Glencorse Burn.

Pentland Hills from Castlelaw Hill

Geology of the Pentland Hills

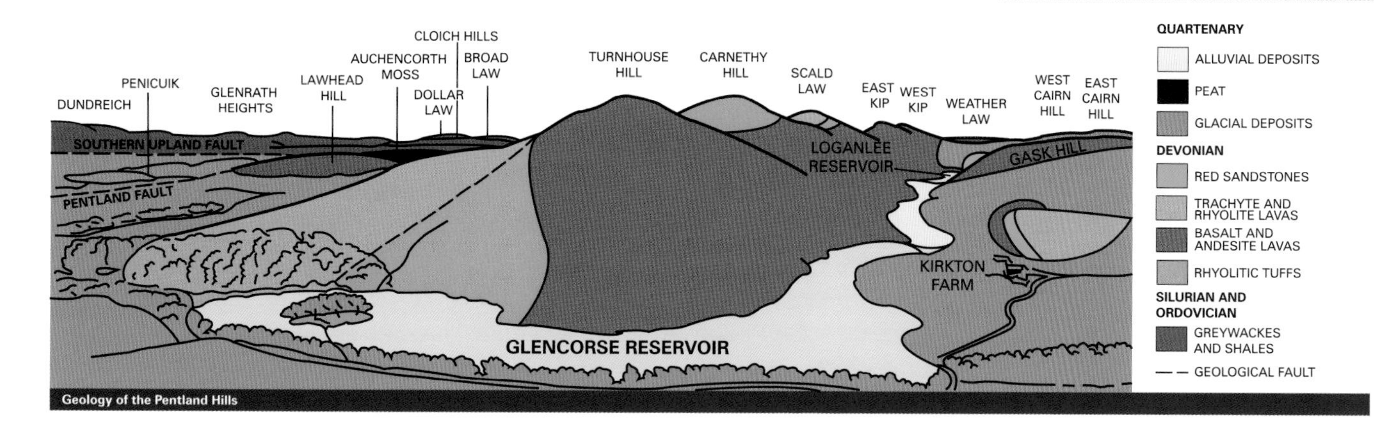

Geology of the Pentland Hills

Looking across Edinburgh from Calton Hill

Today, the city of Edinburgh lies contained between the Firth of Forth to the north and the Pentland Hills to the south, whilst it slowly expands into its fertile farmed hinterland to the east and west.

Our experience of this beautiful city is heavily influenced by the glaciated, undulating landform beneath. The long streets, gently rising and falling across the rolling ridges, provide extensive views out from the city to distant Fife and the Pentland Hills. These fine aspects create a strong sense of openness, reinforced by the many parks and gardens woven into the refined and formal fabric of the townscape. Edinburgh's

Looking down Dundas Street towards the Firth of Forth and Fife

city centre demonstrates this in microcosm, with Arthur's Seat, the Castle Rock and Calton Hill forming prominent focal points, while Princes Street Gardens create a most generous and gracious open space.

The distinctive pattern of Edinburgh's development over the centuries reflects the opportunities and limitations imposed by the landform. Early on, the steep-sided Castle Rock provided an ideal defensive position, spawning a dense huddle of buildings perched above the surrounding wetlands on the 'tail' of rock now known as the Old Town. This contrasts with the spacious rhythm of the later pattern of elegant streets laid out along the east/west alignment of the nearby drumlin ridges. More recent development has focussed on the outskirts, creeping over the farmland towards the by-pass that now forms the defined 'edge' of the modern city.

Looking across Linlithgow nestling in the West Lothian landscape

Millennium Wheel, Falkirk

West of Edinburgh, the rolling landform continues with rich arable farmland and fine estate woodland reflecting both the dry east coast climate and the fertile soils of the underlying Carboniferous rock. Extensive parkland and other designed landscapes laid out by successful industrialists, merchants and land owners complement the large country houses that are a feature of this rural landscape.

Further west, the arable farmland gives way to extensive grassland, fragmented by small shelterbelts and hedgerow trees that form the context for more than 200 years of intensive industrial development. Prominent in this open landscape are the dramatic forms of oil-shale and colliery bings (spoil heaps), slowly being enveloped and softened by woodland. These reminders of past industry lie alongside continuing industrial and residential expansion along the Firth of Forth's southern shores and through the River Almond's low-lying plains, where an extensive transportation network links new development to the major cities of Scotland's Central Belt. Here also, winding its gentle way across the landscape, is the Millennium Link of the newly restored Union Canal.

Sites of Special Scientific Interest (SSSIs)

Hutton's Section, Salisbury Crags

Around 10 Sites of Special Scientific Interest or SSSIs have been notified in the Edinburgh and West Lothian area, reflecting the national and international importance of the local geological and landform resource. Such sites include Arthur's Seat, the Royal Park exposing beautiful sections through the ancient volcano, its intrusions and associated sedimentary rocks. Hutton's Section, located on the flanks of the Arthur's Seat volcano has strong historical resonance, as it was in this vicinity that James Hutton, the acknowledged founder of modern geology, observed sufficient evidence to conclude that the dolerite sill was introduced into the sedimentary layers in a molten state.

Other SSSIs in the Edinburgh area include Agassiz Rock at Blackford Hill, a place visited by Louis Agassiz on 27 October 1840 whilst on a tour of Scotland. He recognised many features which he thought suggested the presence of former glaciers. He is said to have exclaimed during his visit to Blackford Hill "That is the work of ice!" whilst observing the striations or scratches on the rock caused by glaciers.

East Kirkton Quarry SSSI is one of the geological highlights of West Lothian. The strata have yielded fossil evidence for a unique collection of plants and animals including the oldest known complete amphibian and one of the earliest land-dwelling scorpion.

Geological and landform sites are often just as vulnerable to changes in land use as wildlife habitats, so active steps must be taken to ensure that these important sites are safeguarded for the benefit of future generations.

Fossil skeleton of the earliest known reptile *Westlothiana lizziae* popularly known as "Lizzie" found in lower Carboniferous rocks near Bathgate.

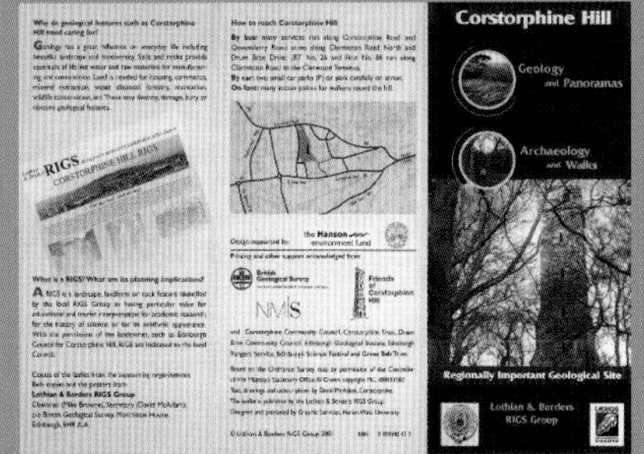

Regionally Important Geological Sites (RIGSs). are sites of local geological interest and value. The Lothian and Borders Group notify RIGS to the local planning authorities, which consult geologists before any development.

It is a requirement that RIGS are used for the public understanding of geology. An example is Corstorphine Hill RIGS, where a dolerite sill intruded into Carboniferous sedimentary strata is well exposed in outcrop and quarries, and superb glaciated pavements on top of the dolerite demonstrate the flow of the recent ice-sheet. Corstorphine Hill RIGS is used for geological walks, as in the Edinburgh Science Festival, and a poster and explanatory leaflet have been prepared.

Other RIGS in the Edinburgh area include: Craigleith Quarry (page 20) from which came the New Town sandstone, Joppa Shore (page 11) Carboniferous sedimentary strata, Dreghorn Cutting (page 10) old red sandstone, Blackford Hill Devonian lavas, and glacial deposits in Roslin Glen. RIGS in West Lothian include the Binny Craig sill and Almondell and Calderwood Country Park showing oil-shale strata and mining.

Corstorphone Hill RIGS:
Left: Edinburgh Science Festival geology walk 1999
Top Right: RIGS poster
Bottom Right: RIGS leflet

Scottish Natural Heritage and the British Geological Survey

Scottish Natural Heritage is a government body. Its aim is to help people enjoy Scotland's natural heritage responsibly, understand it more fully and use it wisely so that it can be sustained for future generations.

Scottish Natural Heritage
12 Hope Terrace
Edinburgh EH9 2AS

The British Geological Survey maintains up-to-date knowledge of the geology of the UK and its continental shelf. It carries out surveys and geological research.
The Scottish Office of BGS is sited in Edinburgh. The office runs an advisory and information service, a geological library and a well-stocked geological bookshop.

British Geological Survey
Murchison House
West Mains Road
Edinburgh EH9 3LA

British Geological Survey
NATURAL ENVIRONMENT RESEARCH COUNCIL

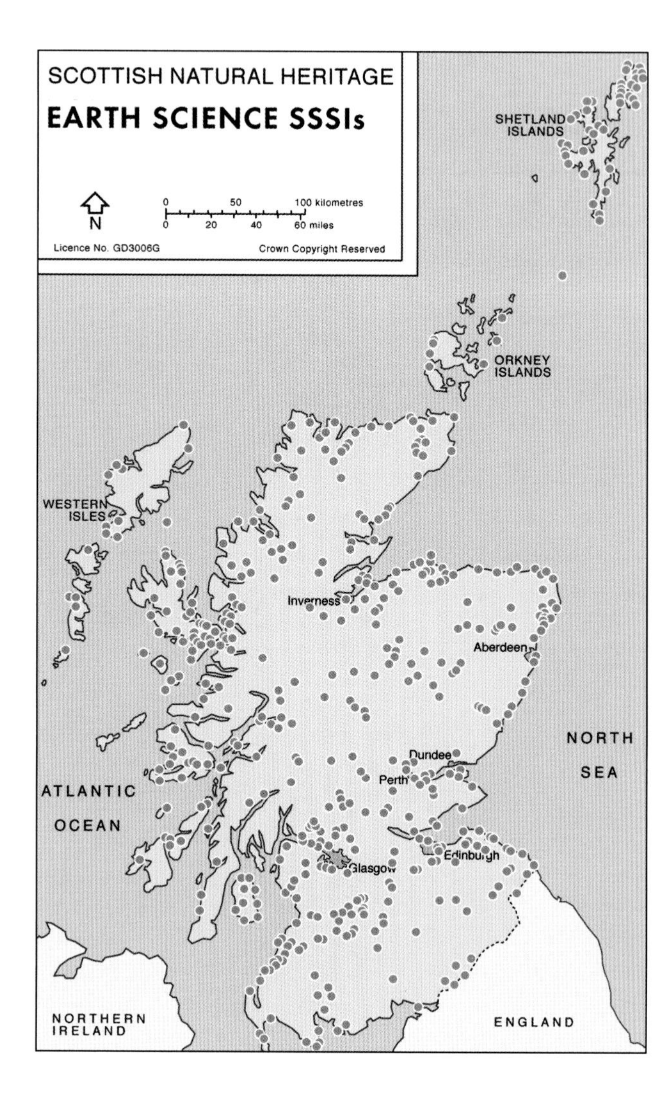

Remember the
Geological Code!
SCOTTISH
NATURAL
HERITAGE
GEOLOGISTS' ASSOCIATION
1858
No need to hammer indiscriminately!
Never collect from walls or buildings.
Keep collecting
to a minimum:
remove fossils, rocks
or minerals only
when essential for
serious study.
And remember to
refer good finds
to local
museums.
The leader of a field
party should ensure
that the spirit of the
code is upheld.
Always seek
permission before
entering
private
land.
No one has the right to "dig out" any site.
Try to leave the site as you found it!
Don't litter fields or roads with rock
fragments, and avoid disturbing plants or wildlife.
Back fill excavations where necessary to
avoid injury to people or animals.
Be considerate, and do not make things
more difficult or hazardous for others
coming after you.
Don't disfigure rock surfaces with brightly
painted numbers, symbols or clusters
of core-holes.
234
SAFETY FIRST!
✔ Wear protective goggles when hammering.
✔ Wear safety hats in quarries or below cliffs.
✔ Avoid loosening rocks on steep slopes.
✗ Do not get cut off by the tide.
✗ Do not enter old mine workings or cave systems.
✗ Do not interfere with machinery in quarries.
● Remember, you are one of several hundred geologists visiting this area every year — so your behaviour *does* matter.
● Please observe the code, so that others can also enjoy the great scenery, geology, and ecology here!
Published by Scottish Natural Heritage, 1996.

Also in the Landscape Fashioned by Geology series...

If you have enjoyed Edinburgh & West Lothian why not find out more about the geology of some of Scotland's distinctive areas in our Landscape Fashioned by Geology series. Each book helps you to explore what lies beneath the soils, trees and heather with clear explanations, stunning photographs and illustrations. The series, which is produced in collaboration with the British Geological Survey, is written by experts in a style which is accessible to all.

Arran and the Clyde Islands

The diverse landscapes of Arran and the Clyde Islands mark the boundary between Highland and Lowland. Discover the ancient secrets and the appeal of these well-loved islands.

David McAdam & Steve Robertson

ISBN 1 85397 287 8 pbk 24pp £3.00

Cairngorms

Their broad plateaux, steep sided glens and deep corries make the Cairngorms one of the foremost mountain landscapes in Britain. Discover how they were fashioned by weathering, glaciers and rivers.

John Gordon, Vanessa Brazier, Rob Threadgold & Sarah Keast

ISBN 1 85397 086 7 pbk 28pp £2.00

East Lothian and the Borders

Underneath the calm facade of south east Scotland's fertile plains and rolling hills lies a complex structure, which reflects an eventful geological history.

David McAdam & Phil Stone

ISBN 1 85397 242 8 pbk 26pp £3.00

Fife and Tayside

The dramatic coastline and volcanic hills of Fife and Tayside are testiment to the dramatic geological past. The story is set at a time when Scotland sat astride the equator.

Mike Browne, Alan McKirdy & David McAdam

ISBN 1 85397 110 3 pbk 36pp £3.95

Loch Lomond to Stirling

The heart of Scotland encompasses some of the most diverse landscapes in Scotland. From the low Carse to the mountain tops - find out how these modern landscapes reflect the geological changes of the past.

Mike Browne & John Mendum

ISBN 1 85397 119 7 pbk 26pp £2.00

Northwest Highlands

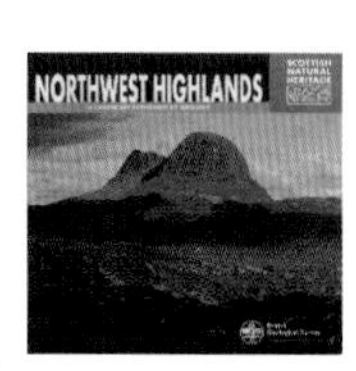

Providing an ancient bulwark to Atlantic storms, the stunning scenery we see today in Northwest Highlands was created by the dramatic collision of continents. This book tells a dramatic tale of Scotland's journey through time - our links to Canada, Greenland and Scandinavia and the exploits of the early geological explorers. In explaining our rocky past, it also shows why this region is so important to geologists today.

John Mendum, Jon Merritt & Alan McKirdy

ISBN 1 85397 139 1 pbk 52pp £6.95

Orkney and Shetland

These northern outposts of Scotland hold a great fascination for the geologist. Starting 3 billion years ago, their story tells of colliding continents, bizarre lifeforms and a landscape which continues to be eroded by the pounding force of the Atlantic.

Clive Auton, Terry Fletcher & David Gould ISBN 1 85397 220 7 pbk 24pp £2.50

Skye

Skye is one of Scotland's most popular tourist destinations, and deservedly so. But what would Skye be without the jagged peaks of the Cuillins or the intriguing rock formations of the Quirang? In many ways it is the geology of Skye that attracts it's visitors and this booklet helps you to understand how the mountains, rocks and lochs were formed.

David Stephenson & Jon Merritt ISBN 1 85397 026 3 pbk 24pp £2.50

Scotland: the creation of its natural landscape

Scotland: the Creation of its Natural Landscape provides a wealth of information on how Scotland was created and the events that took place there through the aeons. But the story doesn't stop back in the mists of time, it continually unfolds and this book provides up to the minute information on geological events taking place beneath our feet, It also provides a history of geological science and highlights the enormous contribution Scots geologists have made to the world.

Alan McKirdy & Roger Crofts ISBN 1 85397 004 2 pbk 64pp £7.50

Series Editor: Alan McKirdy (SNH)

Other books soon to be produced in the series include:

- Mull and Iona • Parallel Roads of Glen Roy • Rum

SNH Publication Order Form

Title	Price	Quantity
Arran & the Clyde Islands	£3.00	
Cairngorms	£2.00	
East Lothian & the Borders	£3.00	
Edinburgh & West Lothian	£4.95	
Fife & Tayside	£4.95	
Loch Lomond to Stirling	£2.00	
Northwest Highlands	£6.95	
Orkney & Shetland	£2.50	
Skye	£3.95	
Scotland: the Creation of its natural landscape	£7.50	

Postage and packaging: free of charge within the UK.

A standard charge of £2.95 will be applied to all orders from the EU.

Elsewhere a standard charge of £5.50 will apply.

Please complete in **BLOCK CAPITALS**

Name ____________________

Address ____________________

____

____

Post Code ____________________

Type of Credit Card VISA ☐ EUROCARD MasterCard ☐

Name of card holder ____________________

Card Number ☐☐☐☐ ☐☐☐☐ ☐☐☐☐ ☐☐☐☐

Expiry Date ☐☐ ☐☐

Send order and cheque made payable to Scottish Natural Heritage to:
Scottish Natural Heritage, Design and Publications, Battleby, Redgorton,
Perth PH1 3EW
E-mail: pubs@redgore.demon.co.uk www.snh.org.uk

We may want to send you details of other SNH publications, please tick the box below if you do not want this. We will not pass your details to anyone else.

I do not wish to receive information on SNH publications ☐

Please add my name to the mailing list for the SNH Magazine ☐

Publications Catalogue ☐